STUFF AND NONSENSE

STUFF AND NONSENSE

and So On

by

WALTER DE LA MARE

With Woodcuts by

BOLD

' Oft on the dappled turf at ease
I sit, and play with similes.'

LONDON
CONSTABLE & CO. LTD
1927

Printed in Great Britain by T. and A. Constable Ltd.
at the University Press, Edinburgh

TO

JAMES HERBERT DE LA MARE

Dear B., dear B., dear B., dear B.,
I dedicate this book to thee.

CONTENTS

TWINERS

MEAT, FISH, ETC.

[ix]

ANIMATED NATURE

MORE TWINERS

THINKERS AND SPECTRES

FAR AND NEAR AND FINIS

TWINERS

' So doth the woodbine, the sweet Honisuckle,
Gently entwist. . . .'

A

MOONSHINE

THERE was a young lady of Rheims,
    There was an old poet of Gizeh ;
He rhymed on the deepest and sweetest of themes,
    She scorned all his efforts to please her :
        And he sighed, ' Ah, I see,
        She and sense won't agree.'
So he scribbled her moonshine, mere moonshine, and she,
With jubilant screams, packed her trunk up in Rheims,
Cried aloud, ' I am coming, O Bard of my dreams ! '
    And was clasped to his bosom in Gizeh.

THE BONNET

THERE was a young man in a hat,
And by went Miss B. in a bonnet ;
When he saw her, he smiled at the lat-
Ter : ay, and the roses upon it.
  But when, by and by—
  As blue as the sky—
  He detected her eye
  'Neath its brim ; well, oh my !
He wished that fair cheek was well under his hat,
And his own half-concealed in her bonnet.

THE TULIP

There was an old Begum of Frome,
There was an old Yogi of Leicester ;
She sent him a tulip in bloom,
He rolled his black eyes and he blessed her.
How replete with delight
Is a flower to the sight !
It brightens the day and it sweetens the night.
Oh ! if all the old ladies grew tulips in Frome,
How happy the Yogis in Leicester !

DEAR SIR

There was an old Rabbi of Ur ;
    He loved a Miss Beaulieu.
She sent him a letter : ' Dear Sir . . . '
Then a stone-cold ' Yours truly.'
        Now what she could mean
        By the dots in between
        Is not plain to be seen.
We can but infer the Rabbi of Ur
    Enquired of Miss Beaulieu.

THE DUET

THERE was a young lady of Tring,
There was an old fellow of Kello ;
And she—she did nothing but sing,
And he—he did nothing but bellow :
    Now I think (and don't you ?)
    That the best thing to do
    Were to marry these two :
Then maybe the one would sing no more in Tring,
Or the other not bellow in Kello.

THE RUBY

THERE was an old Bhoojah of Ghat,
Who wore a prodigious great Ruby—
' Out of sight,' it is said, ' when he sat.'
But how can this possibly true be ?
I 've pondered and pondered, and sometimes have felt
That the gem in discussion reposed in his belt,
For 'tis there if sheer sitting has made one too fat,
And—being a Bhoojah—one sits on a mat,
There *might* blaze unseen a great Ruby.

MISS PHEASANT

THERE was an old man with a gun,
Who espied an old lady named Pheasant;
She sat on a seat in the sun,
And he stared, and he stared—most unpleasant:
But at last, drawing near,
He made it quite clear
That he had no *intention* so rude to appear,
But was merely confused, being out with his gun,
At espying a lady named Pheasant.

HOPPING

There was an old widow of Wapping;
There is sweet pretty country in Kent :
She heard that her friends had gone hopping,
And thought she 'd go too.   So she went.
    Now this simple old dear,
    Who was sixty—and plump,
    Thought a hop, it is clear,
    Is a one-leggèd jump ;
And thus she progressed—hop-hop-hop—hop—through
    Wapping,
    On—on—into sweet pretty Kent.

GREEN

THERE was an old grocer of Goring
Had a butter assistant named Green,
Who sank through a hole in the flooring
And never was afterwards seen.
    Did he look in his cellar ?
    Did he miss the poor fellow ?
    Not at all.   Quite phlegmatic,
    He retired to an attic,
And there watched the moon in her glory o'er Goring—
A sight not infrequently seen.

J. J.

THERE was an old parson of Sinder
Had a sexton named Jeremy Jones,
He'd watch him from out of his winder—
And smile at him digging up bones ;
 Then, hid in a curtain,
 To make sound uncertain,
He'd holla, ' Hello, there ! OLD JONES ! J. Jones ! '
 And Jones, like an owl,
 Would peer o'er his showl,
And wonder from which of his old friends in Sinder
Had burst out that muffled, ' Old Jones ! '

BUTTONS

There was an old skinflint of Hitching
Had a cook, Mrs. Casey, of Cork ;
There was nothing but crusts in the kitchen,
While in parlour was sherry and pork.
So at last, Mrs. Casey, her pangs to assuage,
Having snipped off his buttonses, curried the page ;
And now, while that skinflint gulps sherry and pork
In his parlour adjacent to Hitching,
To the tune blithe and merry of knife and of fork,
Anthropophagy reigns in the kitchen.

MEAT, FISH, ETC.

' I had rather live
With cheese and garlic in a windmill.'

MEAT

FROM out his red and sawdust shop
This butcher, born to chepe and chop,
Surveys without a trace of grief
Perambulating tombs of beef.
From an unmoved and pale-blue eye,
He gloats on these sarcophagi—
Whether they 're walking or riding in 'busses
He gloats on these sarcophaguses,
And as he gloats (with greedy eye)
He says, ' Buy !   Buy !   Buy !   Buy !   Buy !
    Buy ! '

It 's probable we never shall
Convince him that an animal
Is not mere layers of lean and fat ;
He may have butched too much for that.

But still ; some day we may be able
To wean him to the vegetable.
Turnip, potato, parsnip, swede—
If only upon these he 'd feed,
One beast the fewer then might bleed ;
He 'd be less butcherous than of yore
And help the greengrocer next door.

FISH

In June it must be very nice
To bask about a block of ice—
And watch the World go broiling by
Under a hot and windless sky ;
Then turn aside, and, sniffing, see
Perennial mounds of shrimps for tea ;
How genial, too, when fancying dab,
To slip one from one's marble slab ;
Or, when the stars begin to twinkle,
To broach an unofficial winkle ;
Or to descend in morning slipper
And not to have to *buy* a kipper.
This must be very pleasant, and
As pleasant, too, to understand,
When you have cod—are dining off it—
You 're only eating so much profit.
Solacing thoughts like these must stir
The musings of the Fishmonger.

IRON

It is the gentle poet's art
In pleasing diction to impart
    Whatever he thinks meet ;
And even make the ugly bloom
    In splendour at our feet.
But neither Shelley, Keats nor Byron
Sang songs on Zinc, or odes to Iron :
    Impracticable feat !

When passing, then, I always bow
To him who makes (I know not how)
A living out of sinks and pails—
    I bow across the street—
Just bow : and then my courage fails :
    I beat a swift retreat.

For who can help but ponder on
His awful state when, Sunday gone,
    At daybreak bleak and chill,
He turns the shop-key in its lock,
Stares in upon his ghastly stock
    And opens Monday's till.

THE BARDS

My agèd friend, Miss Wilkinson,
    Whose mother was a Lambe,
Saw Wordsworth once, and Coleridge, too,
    One morning in her p'ram'.*

Birdlike the bards stooped over her—
    Like fledgling in a nest ;
And Wordsworth said, ' Thou harmless babe ! '
    And Coleridge was impressed.

The pretty thing gazed up and smiled,
    And softly murmured, ' Coo ! '
William was then aged sixty-four
    And Samuel sixty-two.

* This was a three-wheeled vehicle
    Of iron and of wood ;
It had a leather apron,
    But it hadn't any hood.

THE TANK

' IF I had a little money,' mused the Rev. Philip Fish,
' And could buy (without a scruple) any little thing I wish,
I would purchase an Aquarium, some moss and ferns and
      sand,
Some pretty shining pebbles, branching coral, sea-shells, and

At centre, a small cistern—made of glass—and placed,
    well, *so*,
        And filled with what in France is known as *eau.*

' It 's really very singular ; as soon as I 'm asleep,
My dreams at once commit me to the wonders of the deep ;

I wallow with the whale, or in profundities obscure
Disport with shapes no waking eye for terror could endure.
At times I am an octopus ; at times I am a sprat,
And there *is* a lot of ocean for a little fish like that !

' I had an uncle—Phineas Fish ; but now that he 's
        deceased
All hope of a small legacy has practically ceased.
But if a rich parishioner should tactfully suggest,
" Now, tell me, Father Fish, what little present you 'd
        like best,"
Although I wouldn't *think* of it—could only smile my
        thanks,
            I 'm sure, you know, my thoughts would turn to
                tanks.'

BISHOP WINTERBOURNE

THE Rev. William Winterbourne,
When walking in the Mall,
Tired of genteel pedestrians,
Much yearned to meet a *pal*,
Or, failing an old crony,
    His best gal.

Beelzebub decoyed that wish up ;
The Reverend William 's now a bishop.
Now, when he fares down Piccadilly,
His blameless Conscience—willy-nilly—
So arch-episcopally staid is,
He never gives a thought to ladies.
Heedless of impious scrutinies
The curious fix on all D.D.'s,

His gaiters 'neath his apron wend ;
His steps in one direction bend ;
His heart, as right as reverend,
Has for desire one only end—

To wit, to join the wild *Te Deum*
That echoes through the Athenaeum.

HYSSOP

SAID Judge Jessop,
' The hyssop
You *think*'s in your wall,
Correctly
And strictly
Isn't hyssop at all.'
' Isn't hyssop ? ' says I ;
' Isn't hyssop,' says he ;
' By no means—not hyssop at all.'

' If my hyssop,
Judge Jessop,
Isn't hyssop at all,
Tell me truly
And duly
Why it grows on my wall ! '
' Why it grows on ? ' says he.
' Yes, it grows on,' says I ;
' Why it grows and it grows on my wall.'

' On the Bisop,'
Said Judge Jessop,
' (With the h out), we 'll call,
And straightly,
Sedately,
We 'll resort to your wall.'

'With a ladder?' says I,
'With a ladder,' says he;
'And we'll ask him—"What's *that* in the wall?"'

So the Bisop,
Judge Jessop
And me—three in all—
Hell and leather
Together
Climbed up on my wall.
'What's that there?' says I.
'What's what where?' says he;
'Why, house-leek,' said the Bisop.   That's all.

MISS CLEGG

Miss Clegg was accustomed to do as she wished,
Upon Fate she was never a waiter ;

And whenever she came upon water she fished,
And always attired in a gaiter.

The word has a singular look, I agree,
Yet is apt in the case of Miss Clegg ;

Since from birth she a monopode happened to be,
  And you can't wear a pair on one leg.

Her foot was her basis then, while with her float
  She dangled a worm 'neath a willow ;
Or, far out to sea, stood erect in a boat,
  And awaited a bite from the billow.

THE LADY GODIVA

The Lady Godiva Godolphin, of a blood by the centuries
   blued,
        Flowing back, I believe,
        To Adam and Eve,
     Had a rooted disdain of the *nood*.

'Sheep are clad,' she would cry, 'in their woollies;
   the buffalo's hirsute, though rude;

Apart from their tails,
Even flounders have scales ;
Not a shrimp in the ocean swims nood.

' The ruff has a ruff, though a ruff 's not enough ; the sea-
lion, I 'm told, has a hood ;
The lobster a back
It 's an effort to crack,
And the zebra with stripes is imbrued.

' The oyster is shelled, and the goat has a coat, whether
wild, or domestic or Zoo'ed.
From a bee to a bear—
You can look, you can stare—
But in nature *no* creature is nood.'

Pelisses and petticoats, tippets and jupes, she wore
by the gross (when she could),
She would ride in her gig
In nine fronts and three wig,
And smile when the little boys boo'ed.

Her tables and chairs and her bedsteads, lest even their
toes should obtrude,
She sewed up in chintz
Trimmed with calico, since,
Thus upholstered, they couldn't look nood.

[28]

The Cherubs, that graced the Godolphins at rest in the
Church of St. Jude,
She said, looked less bloated,
When trousered and coated,
And at all events none remained nood.

When her bath-tub was brought by a handmaid, who at
no time desired to intrude,
She would paddle, splash, plunge—
In a sark made of sponge,
And not, as do most of us, nood.

Now it 's whispered the Lady Godiva was the least little
bit of a prude ;
I really can't say,
She long since passed away,
And what matter if nobody knoowed ?

AN IDLE WORD

I USED to wear a diamond ring,
A small but valuable thing,
A souvenir of how and when
I had succeeded up till then.
I used to wear it day and night,
I polished it to keep it bright.
I never took it off.   I 'd sit
For hours at home and look at it.
For years and years I 'd had to wait
To make it mine.   It kept me straight.

When, too, in shops I 've sat at tea,
People would stare at it and me—
Not knowing *who* I might not be.
I 'd just call, ' Miss ! '—the waitress would
Scamper to bring me drink and food.
Then with my hand I 'd smooth my hair,
Knowing my diamond safely there.

Oft, too, when walking in the street
' Aha ! ' I 've thought (the thought was sweet),
' They little guess what 's lying hid
' Beneath this glove ! ' (of suède or kid).

If only I 'd been let alone,
I 'd have stayed happy with that stone.

But no.　In this world there are them
Who envy even a gem.
One day I heard a lady say—
And as she spoke, she looked my way :
' A diamond is a vulgar thing
To see coruscking in a ring ;
And, like as not, as I 've been told,
They 're only glass—in brass—not gold.'

I rose ;　I felt, without a doubt,
My very life-blood trickling out.
I sold the ring, at awful loss,
To one I knew named Isaac Moss.
And now in life no hope I see ;
Its bottom 's fallen out for me.

My situation 's gone ;　I owe
Not less than twenty pounds or so ;
Outside a Public House I stand,
With loafers upon either hand ;
And if a Constable draws near,
My skin goes cold and stiff with fear ;
He knows I know he 's but to wait
And some dark cell will be my fate.

It only proves—what good men teach—
We should be cautious in our speech.

If that proud lady had not said
My diamond of glass was made,
Should I be drifting in my prime
Into a *cul-de-sac* of crime ?
One heedless, scoffing word—and see !
What that old vixen 's done for me !

ANIMATED NATURE

                        Th' unwieldy elephant
To make them mirth us'd all his might, and wreath'd
His lithe proboscis.

HORSES

I NEVER see a coach go by
Without remembering that I
Shall some day take a ride in one
With horses not allowed to run.
They 'll step on leisurely to where
A hole gapes in the open air,
Then turn and look, to see if they
May now enjoy a munch of hay,
Or any other kind of meal.
It 's odd how little horses feel.
Half their delight on earth one knows is
To have us humans pat their noses.
And when at last we go our way,
They don't so much as breathe a Nay ;
But, if permitted, on will pass,
To graze upon our funeral grass.

BAH !

WHEN I chanced to look over the wall in the glade—
    I was taking a walk with Mamma—
I saw an old ewe sitting down in the shade,
    And she opened her mouth and said, ' Bah ! '

That 's always what happens when sheep I come near,
    They watch me approach from afar,
And out of the turnips and clover I hear
    A horrid ironical ' Bah ! '

What can I have done ?   I can't understand—
    The cantankerous creatures they are !
I never throw stones, I hold dear Mamma's hand,
    And I don't think they *ought* to say ' Bah ! '

SAID JANE

SAID Jane to the old Fisherman,
     ' I cannot understand
Why ever little fishes swim
     So close up to the land ;
If *I* knew of those horrid hooks
     I 'd keep away from *sand*.'

That Fisherman, he scratched his head
     ('Twas sunset o'er the lea),
Then twisted of his quid, and said,
     ' What, missie, boffles *me*
Is why the little warmits keep
     A sight too far to sea.'

And there the problem must remain—
     Beyond the wit of man—
As posited by little Jane
     And by the Fisherman,
Leaving it still precisely as
     When they their talk began.

THE WAIF

There lived a small hermaphrodite beside the silver Brent,
A stream meandering not in maps of Surrey, Bucks, or
    Kent ;
Yet jealous elves from these sweet parts, this tiny mite
    to vex,
Would tease, torment, and taunt, and call him, ' Master
    Middlesex ! '

He lived on acorns, dewdrops, cowslips, bilberries, and
    snow—
A small, shy, happy, tuneful thing, and innocent of woe ;
Except when these malignant imps, his tenderness to vex,
Would tease, torment, and taunt, and call him, ' Master
    Middlesex ! '

He ran away ; he went to sea ; to far Peru he came.
There where the Ataquipa flows and odorous cinchona
    blows and no one knows his name,
He nests now with the humming-bird that sips but never
    pecks ;
And silent slides the silver Brent, and mute is Middlesex.

THE SEA-NYMPH

THERE was an old mariner
Heard 'mid his dunes
A swallow-tailed sea-nymph
Descanting of tunes ;
Trill, grace-note, cadenza,
And high in the treble,
She warbled as sweet
As a sea-nymph is able.

He hearkened, he pondered,
He said, ' I 'm aware
Of the strains of a sea-nymph
Seducing the air ;
No doubt she sits combing
And sleeking her hair.
She sings like a linnet,
I feel certain she 's fair,
And she *may* be supposing
That *I* 'm lurking near !
But of music I 've little,
Of voice I have none,
I can merely applaud
When the aria is done.'

So he sate on the dunes
By the fringe of the deep,

And, lulled by her warblings,
He fell fast asleep.
When he woke, 'twas cold night
With huge stars overhead,
But all silent the sands
Of his barbarous bed.

He sighed—oh, sighed softly :
' My applause will come late,
For I see that the sea-nymph
Was unable to wait ;
Still, good manners must not by
Inaction be sapped ' ;
So he clap-clap-clap-clap-clap-
Clap-clap-clap-clap-clapped.

NO !

FULL oft I 've stood at winter dusk alone upon the strand,
Watching the breakers thundering in for leagues across
    the sand,
And smiled up at my friend in heaven, the Moon, so pale
    and wan,
        Amused within that wise men say
        'Tis she who, gliding on her way,
           'Tis *She*—who leads them on !

No, no.   And when at dead of dark—and that sweet
    orb 's at rest—
I muse for hours on Rigel, Deneb, Spica, and the rest
Of Night's clear candles gleaming there like glow-worms
    in the grass,
        I laugh aloud to think of those
        Who, peering through a tube, suppose
           They 're pits of boiling gas !

Away with them !   I dance and sing ; but could not sing
　　at all,
Believing me mere matter on a rotatory Ball.
Such horrid thoughts confuse my mind, they fill my soul
　　with woe ;
　　　　　But when in meadows green I stray,
　　　　　　　Between the dawning and the day,
　　　　　　　And hear the lark's shrill roundelay,
　　　　　　　I *know* I ᴋɴᴏᴡ I KNOW.

ANN'S AUNT AND THE BEAR

IT filled Ann's Aunt Maria with rage
To see a wild thing in a cage.
At sight of creature, winged or furred,
Confined by bars, by chains deterred,
She 'd melt with pity ; in a word—
' Pore thing,' she 'd cry, ' you pore, *pore* thing ! '
At which the dainty dear would sing
A little soft sad song, or cheep,
Or turn a curious eye to peep
At her great face, and brow, and bonnet—
Like a cathedral perched upon it.
'Twas just her kindly, friendly humour :
She 'd grieve as much o'er lion or puma,
And gloat upon their keepers when
They chanced their heads within its den.
' Pore thing ! ' she 'd mutter, not ' Poor Men ! '

One afternoon her aunt and Ann
(Who 'd gone to see a nursery-man
About a leaky watering can),
As they were moving gently home,
On a most horrid scene did come :
Two foreigners (with longish hair)
Were leading on a chain a Bear,
A bushy, bright-eyed, thirsty beast,

[44]

Who had trudged a score of miles at least
In heat and dust—at least a score,
And danced perhaps as many more ;
Yes, danced—and growled—and danced again
Whene'er these long-haired foreign men
Should in their cruelty think proper
To try and earn an English copper,
Or tuppence, even, if any dunce
Should want the dance danced more than once.

Yes, there, beneath a chestnut's shade,
This parched-up beast was being made
To caper and to growl a noise
To please a pack of errand boys ;
It danced and gruffed, it breathed vast sighs,
Its half-bald head a maze of flies ;
Its claws went tic-tac in the dust,
And still it danced, for dance it must ;
While the two Frogs in hope of gain
Stood grinning by and tweaked its chain.

When Ann, and Ann's aunt, Aunt Maria,
Saw this, Ann's aunt's eyes flashed with fire ;
She said, ' Pore thing ! you pore, pore thing ! '
And then she raised a stout umbrella,
And *turned* upon the nearest fellow.
French or Italian, Greek or Dutch,
She simply couldn't thwack too much ;

Sound thumping thumps she laid full many on,
Then up and smote his dazed companion.

And there you see kind Aunt Mari',
Her bugled bonnet all awry,
And plump cheek flushed with her exertions
Against these parasitic Persians ;
While Ann, now lost in rapture, stands
Clapping her little mittened hands,
And butcher's, baker's, grocer's boy
Yell out their rude and barbarous joy.

Alack ! what evil chance we find !
Her wrath made Aunt Maria blind :
In compassing his tyrants' ruin,
She didn't notice their poor Bruin,
Who, having wriggled off his muzzle,
Was shuffling in to join the tussle,
And, rather giddy in the head,
In gratitude for what she had said
And done to that cruel Bruin-baster,
Went sidling up, and then—embraced her.

It 's sad indeed to have to tell
What then this kind, kind soul befell—
Ann's Aunt Maria.   So sharp B's squeeze
Ann hadn't time to whisper, ' Please,
You 're cuddling my dear aunt so close
You must be treading on her toes,

Supple and gay, he sleeks his way,
   And—gollops up poor Edward.
' Oh, Esmeralda, shun delay,
   And hasten quickly bedward ! '

Alas ! she lingers ; and too long.
   A pounce, a far, faint squealin',
The young and fair are now the strong,
   And much refresht 's the feline.

D

MORE TWINERS

. . . The female Ivy so
Enrings the bosky fingers of the Elme.

VERY

THERE was a young lady of Bow,
A dandy there was, too, of Derry ;
' How sweetly the hawthorn trees blow ! '
He murmured.   And she replied, ' Very.'
    Then she glanced, and she smiled,
    And she tapped with her shoe ;
    Then slid her eyes sidelong,
    And both were pure blue ;
    And the longer the silence,
    The deeper it grew :
    Till he said, ' If 'twere kissing,
    I 'd like to kiss *you.*
Would it be very naughty to do—well—like—so ? '
She thought him a goose, yet she didn't cry, ' Bo ! '
But blushed, tittered, sighed, and said, ' Very ! '

FRECKLES

THERE was a young lady of Beccles,
Who had a twin sister in Crete,
She was dappled all over with freckles,
From her top-knot right down to her feet ;
For round about Gnossos the sun is so hot
One sits in a torpor, complexion forgot,
And basks in the bountiful heat.
Now the Beccles young damosel,
Being a twin,
Soon reflected the state
Her poor sister was in,
Though never a word came from Crete ;
But she being taller,
The freckles were smaller,
And stopped inches short of her feet.

THE BLACKBIRDS

There was an old man, in reproof
Of the blackbirds hob-nob in his cherries,
Cried : ' Be off now, you rascals, be off ! '
But the rogues never stirred from the berries.
  They knew that his wits
  Were a little astray ;
  They knew on old fogeys it 's
  Easy to prey.
So they merely sang sweeter to drown his reproof,
And the louder he called at them, ' Rascals, be off ! '
  The merrier they in his cherries.

THE PENNY

A PERSON of Abergavenny
Met an old man from Bromley-by-Bow ;
He said, ' Would you lend me a penny ? '
And she, she replied, ' I don't know.'
Now strangers are dangerous, that we agree ;
And with money in public best not be too free.
Still, perchance 'twere less caustic to say, ' Well, I 'll see,'
Than that vague ' I don't know,'
When asked for a penny in Abergavenny
By an old man from Bromley-by-Bow.

WOOL

THERE was an old lady of Poole
Who called at a mercer's in Whitting,
And ordered £10 worth of wool,
When 'twas *weight* she required—for her knitting.
    Now her nephews and nieces
    Look like sheep in their fleeces ;
    Their feet sound like trotters,
    When out with their mothers ;
    When they 're drinking and eating,
    Their talk is all bleating ;
And many a glutton has thought of boiled mutton
When watching their capers in school.

KANT

THERE was an old Lawyer of Diss,
There was an old Doctor of Bicester ;
They argued if that there is This,
Then the Thing-in-Itself is a twister.
    When an agèd old aunt,
    Of philosophy scant,
    Said such talk was all cant :
Then her nephews indulged in contortions of bliss,
And one of 'em up and, yes, kissed her.

ERGO

THERE was an old man said, ' I am :
And therefore, O rapture ! I think ! '
They retorted, ' H'm, h'm ? ' and ' H'm, h'm ! '
And each at the rest winked a wink.
 Yet it may be, you know,
 That he *fancied* it so—
 That he 'd taken to heart
 The words of Descartes,
Who, hoping and hoping for *something* to come,
At last had exclaimed, ' *Cogito, ergo sum.*'
Yes, it may be he had not intended a cram,
 Or to give an occasion to wink,
When he piped up in ecstasy, ' Neighbours, I am :
 And therefore I think ! '

THE SHUBBLE

THERE was an old man said, ' I fear
   That life, my dear friends, is a bubble,
Still, with all due respect to a Philistine ear,
   A limerick 's best when it 's double.'
   When they said, ' But the waste
      Of time, temper, taste ! '
He gulped down his ink with cantankerous haste,
   And chopped off his head with a shubble.

THINKERS AND SPECTRES

'Is such a think as this allowed to live?'

MEDDLING

Says James to his second cousin, he says,
      ' Fair mystery, John, it be,
Where them that thinks get the thoughts they thinks—
      What they calls philosophee ;
I sits on these sands for days at a stretch,
      Staring out at the deep blue Sea,
But, pickle me, Coz, if a glim there comes
      Of the thoughts what they thinks to *me*.'

Says John, nodding solemn, 'There's men and there's men,
      And there 's some keeps their minds on the latch ;
But if ever you pines for to fish down deep,
It 's got to be done when you 're half asleep,
      And with tackle and hook to match.
And I warn you, James, when you gets a bite,
      It 's turrible things you 'll catch ;
Fishes with goggle eyes, fishes with wings,
Fishes with beards and electric stings,
Shapeless, elastic and jellified things,
      No Christian could despatch.

' What 's worse,' says he, ' and I 've seed it in books
      On *most* peculiar themes,
If you hankers to know what a willain you are,
      Keep a werry sharp eye on your dreams.

Look at 'em close, James, and you 'll find
You 've got a fair horrible sink of a mind,
    Like a bog in a fog that steams.

' But never no good come of meddling, James,
    There 's things as is *hid*, I say ;
Take it or leave it, then, just as you please,
There 's nothing what 's round us here—he's or she's—
But lives on a soo-per-fish-i-es,
    And there I intend to stay.'

THE ACCOMPANIMENT

THE man in the hat (whom you see in the picture)
    Mused softly one evening : ' I sit in this copse,
And the birds warble sweetly, for sweet is their nature ;
    Yet they sing at haphazard, then every one stops.

' Yes, as if at the lift of a baton or finger,
    The love-notes, *pu-wees*, and *to-witta-woos* cease,
Not a pause for applause, not a wing seems to linger,
    The forests fall mute—the whole world is at peace.

' I marvel.   I marvel.   For take, now, the linnet—
    That sociable haunter of charlock and gorse,
There is no sweeter throat with a melody in it,
    Still, *solo* he sang as a matter of course !

' God forbid that with drum, cornet, triangle, cymbal,
    We should drown the wee cherubs : assuredly not.
Still, my dear sister Jane on the harp is still nimble,
    Nor have I my old skill with the fiddle forgot. . . .'

So now, as the sun in the West is declining,
    The twain to that hill hie, the birds hie there too ;
Rings the plucking of harp-strings, the cat-gut's sweet
      pining,
    And a chorus *orchestral* ascends in the blue.

Besides which, a host of all small kinds of beasties,
　　(They are shown on the cut, though Miss Jane's out
　　　　of sight),
Having learned the harmonic a marvellous feast is,
　　Troll out an *Amen* ere they part for the night.

WHY ?

' DEAR Father, tell me, Why are Worms ? '
    Tim questioned me ; and I—
Mute as a fish, stared on and on
    Into the empty sky.

' Father, dear, tell me, *Why* are Worms ? '
    Tim questioned me.   Poor me !
In vain, in vain, I gazed, gazed, gazed
    Over the vacant sea.

' O Father ! father ! How are Worms ?
    And When ?—and What ?—and Where ? '
I scanned the mute and wintry blue,
    The cloudlets floating there ;
I scanned the leafless trees that tossed
    Their twiglets in the air ;

I marked the rooks and starlings stalk
　　Up—down the furrows bare ;
I passed an unresponsive hand
　　Over my hatless hair ;

But when these eyes encountered Tim's,
　　Mine was the emptier stare.

SUPPOSE

Suppose the year were but a month,
    And that a week,
    And that a day :
At thought of it I scarce can speak ;
    The difference, I say !
In four-and-twenty hours to see,
Like phantoms in a dream flit by,
Between the smiling earth and sky,
A whole year's birds, flowers, seasons fair,
Packed in a space so small, so spare,
    The gross rapidity !
It simply makes my head go round,
It lifts me dizzy from the ground,
    The mere idea, *per se*.

PONJOO

My Uncle Jasper in Siam
Once breakfasted on Ponjoo jam.
This Ponjoo is a fruit, I find,
That has its pulp outside its rind,
 In colour a pale puce.
Within it lurks a heart-shaped stone
As hard as granite, iron, or bone,
 And round it wells its juice.

Now Uncle was a man of fashion
 Just visiting Siam ;
And when he stripped away the pulp
And took the kernel at a gulp,
He flew into a furious passion
 And said the bad word ' ——— ! '

The Emperor, whose palace stood
Within the fragrant Ponjoo wood,
Sitting at lattice, stooped and heard
My uncle use this wicked word,
 And to his menials said :
' Convey that Pagan to a cell
Where never Echo's voice shall tell
The language that just now befell,
 And there strike off his head.'

[71]

And that is why our Family,
At early breakfast, lunch, or tea,
    And I, where'er I am,
If on the table we see laid
A pot of Ponjoo marmalade,
Say, ' Drat it,' to the parlourmaid,
    But never, never ' —— ! '

THE SPECTRE

The moment I glanced at the mirk-windowed mansion
    that lifts from the woodlands of Dankacre, Lincs.,
To myself I said softly : ' Confide in me, pilgrim, why is
    it the heart in your bosom thus sinks ?
What 's amiss with this region ?   It 's certainly England ;
    the moon, there, is rising, and there Vega blinks.'

A drear wind sighed bleakly ; it soughed in the silence ;
    it sobbed as if homesick for Knucklebone, Notts. ;
The moon with her mountains showed spectral and sullen ;
    the corncrake and nightjar craked, jarred, from their
    grots ;
And aloft from its mistletoe nest in an oak-tree, a
    scritch-owlet's scritch froze my blood into clots.

I called on my loved one asleep 'neath the myrtles whose
    buds turn to berries in Willowlea, Herts. ;
I mused on sweet innocent scenes where in summer the
    deer browse, the doves croon, the butterfly darts ;
But, alas ! these devices proved vain, horror loured, my
    terror was such as no metre imparts.

For afar o'er the marshes the booming of bitterns, like the
    bitterns that boomed once from Bootle in Lancs.,
Came mingled with wailings from Dowsing and Dudgeon
    of sea-gulls lamenting o'er Bluddithumbe Banks—

My bowels turned to water; my knees shook; my skin
   crept; and the hairs on my cranium rose up in hanks.

And lo! from an attic, there peered out a visage, with
   eyes like brass bed-knobs and beak like a hawk's;
And it opened the casement, and climbed down the ivy,
   with claws like a trollop's, on legs like a stork's;
And I screamed and fled inland, from mansion and moonshine, till I saw the sun rising on Pep-y-gent, Yorks.

[74]

BONES

SAID Mr. Smith, ' I really cannot
   Tell you, Dr. Jones—
The most peculiar pain I 'm in—
   I think it 's in my *bones*.'

Said Dr. Jones, ' Oh, Mr. Smith,
   That 's nothing. Without doubt
We have a simple cure for that ;
   It is to take them out.'

He laid forthwith poor Mr. Smith
   Close-clamped upon the table,
And, cold as stone, took out his bone
   As fast as he was able.

[75]

And Smith said, ' Thank you, thank you, thank you,'
    And wished him a Good-day ;
And with his parcel 'neath his arm
    He slowly moved away.

THE JILT

WHEN, in her shift, poor Delia Swift
    Heard footfall on the stair,
She whispered low into the house :
      'Who 's there ? '

Her blood stood still from cheek to heel,
    When, softer than a sigh,
Sang in her ear, forlorn and drear,
      ' 'Tis I ! '

'What have you come for ?　Oh, for whom ? '
    The quiet stagnant grew :
And a voice like the wind in the chimney wailed,
      ' For *you* ! '

The room fell bitter cold, her bed
    Multangular became ;
The zig-zag pattern on curtain and wall
    Jigged in the candle flame ;
And Delia, now to panic moved,
Mindless of what a jilt she 'd proved,
Cried out on all the loves she 'd loved,
      By name.

On—on—she pleaded ; vowed ; and wept.
    She pleaded, wept, in vain.
The Spectre catched her, came a lift,
And never seen was she (or shift)
            Again.

FALSE DAWN

My old friend, Lord O., owned a parcel of land—
A waste of wild dunes, rushes, marran and sand—
With a square Tudor mansion—not a bush, not a tree—
Looking over salt flats a full league to the sea ;
     And at his demise he bequeathed it to me.

It was dusk as I entered, a gull to its mates
Cackled high in the air as I passed through the gates,
And out of the distance—full twenty miles wide—
Came the resonant boom of the incoming tide :
     Gulls' scream and ground-swell, and nothing beside.

In the cold of the porch I tugged at the bell,
Till the bowels of the house echoed back like a knell.
I hearkened ; then peered through the hole in the lock ;
And a voice, cold and clammy, inquired, ' Did you knock ? '
     And there was Lord O. in his funeral smock.

In silence he watched me, then led me upstairs
To a room where a table stood, flanked by two chairs ;
For light but a dip, in an old silver stick,
With guttering grease and a long unsnuffed wick ;
     And he said, ' If you 're hungry, eat quick.'

So I sipped his cold water and nibbled his bread,
While he gazed softly out from the holes in his head :—
' You would hardly believe, Brown, when once I was gone,
How I craved for your company—where there is none ;
    Shivered and craved—on and on.

' This house, I agree, may seem cheerless to you ;
But glance from that window !   By Gad, what a view !
And think, when we weary of darkness and rats,
We can share the long night with the moon and the bats,
    And wander for hours on those flats.

' And when in the East creeping daybreak shows wan,
You 'll excuse me, I know, if I have to be gone,
For as soon as sounds cock-crow, the red and the grey,
It 's a rule with us all—even peers must obey—
    We all have to hasten away.'

So that is my fate now.   The small hours draw near,
We shall stalk arm-in-arm in that scenery drear ;
Tête-à-tête by blanched breakers discuss on and on
If it 's better to be flesh and blood or mere bone,
    Till it 's time for Lord O. to be gone.

Yet, doubtless he means well.   I would not suggest
To shun peers with property always is best.

[80]

But insomnia, nightmare, tic-douloureux, cramp,
Have reduced me to what 's little short of a scamp ;
For I 've hung in my hen-roost a very large lamp.
And now, well, at least two full hours before day,
      Lord O., he hears cock-crow, the red and the grey,
      Sighs ; stares at the ocean—and hastens away.

FAR AND NEAR AND FINIS

'There's something in a flying horse,
  There's something in a huge balloon . . .'

THE JOLLIES

The Captain, he said to his Passenger, '"Twill-a be Full
    Moon to-night,
And at Six Bells sharp, by yon transom and the trucks !
    the Jollies will heave in sight ;
And if I was a man and a Christian as would deign for to
    cargo be,
I 'd scuttle to my cabin and I 'd down and say my prayers,
    for the Jollies is a sight to see ! '

The Passenger looked at the Captain, his cheek grey,
    green, and white,
And he stuttered at the scuppers, ' Oh, thank you, Captain
    Stingo, I should much enjoy the sight ' ;
Then descended, like cold suet, to his cabin, and sate in
    the dusk on his bunk,
And (if the English language here admitted of it) he
    thunk and thunk and *thunk*.

And at Five Bells sharp of that there Middle Watch, that
    ship she gave a lurch,
With a noise like the falling of a steeple with all that hangs
    inside it on a church.
And the Passenger ran like a rabbit, his whiskers stiff as
    bristles on his cheek,
And he peered with his eyes above the binnacle, and he
    hadn't very far for to seek.

For to larboard and to starboard was the Jollies—wan,
    green waves mountain-high,
All silvery and haggard, and a-roaring and a-screaming
    under the pitch-black sky ;
Boiling like a pot full of snow-bright broth with a rim full
    nine miles wide ;
And the green Moon gloated on the Passenger while he
    stared at the Jollies—and cried.

And the Captain, he said to the helmsman, ' One course
    I 've ever took,
And that breast-forward, like R. Browning in the poem ;
    so keep her by the book ' ;
And the Captain, he said to his Passenger, ' Look around,
    and you 'll agree,
There seems to be a Jonah stowed away aboard this ship,
    and by Davy, thou beest he ! '

And the Passenger, now past hollering, from his waistcoat
    took his silver pen,
And wrote, ' I leave the all I have to Stingo, kindest and
    best of men.'
And Stingo, having long since a conviction that where
    there 's a Will there 's a Way,
Stood a-smilin' and a-smilin' till the ship was on her beam
    ends, and then he yelled, ' Belay ! '

' Good-bye,' he sobbed, ' my *dear* Mr. Robinson, it 's sad
    to think that parting is so near,
I hoped you might be staying on to breakfast ; no chance
    of that, I fear.'

And the Bo'sun piped shrill upon his whistle ; and a four-
    foot-thick A.B.
Just lifted Mr. Robinson as gently as a babby, and dropped
    him in the sea.

And a Mermaid swimming quiet by the combings, where
    the keelson hawse-pipe yares,
Inwedged him to her bosom like a porpoise at its weaning,
    and soothed away his cares;
And Stingo, thus bereft of Mr. Robinson, yelled, ' Ho,
    there, lay her by !
For by Davy and by Golly she 's a match for any Jolly,
    and there 's Rum for them that 's dry ! '

THE PRETENDER

In the greens of the wilds of Seringapatam
Is the haunt of an ancient redoubtable ram,
    With sharp-pointed horns on its head ;
When it snuffs out a Brahmin it scoops with its hooves,
Till the jungle around it is jungle in grooves,
    And then it pretends to be dead.

O White Man beware of such tactics as these,
For if in compassion thou sink to thy knees,
    All thought of mere safety forgot,
With a jerk of its horns the fell creature comes to,
And smiles, as if saying, ' Ah, friend, is it you ? '
    When there 's none to reply, ' It is not.'

AHKH

At full moon in cold Khamchatka,
  Where the Wheelagheelah flows,
That aquatic fowl, the Vhatka,
  Softly tippets on its toes
(Inebriate with her love-light,
      I suppose).
It is then the astute Khamchatkan
      Fowling goes.

But when her dwindling quarter
  Has to dark her disc resigned,
'Tis a job, by Gob, to slaughter
  A fowl no eye can find—
And his ' Ahkh,' his ' Ahkh ' is nothing
      But a blind.

Now it 's nearer, sweeter, clearer ;
  Now it wails and wanes and dies ;
Now the night-beleaguered hearer
  Hears it ahkhing in the skies ;
When, in sooth, it 's nesting snugly in a nest
      not half its size,
Hidden in the reeds and rushes, scarce a hand's-
      breadth from his eyes !

So the Fowler should go fowling,
   Armed with candle, book, and bell,

When Khamchatka's gleamy crescent
   Casts a beamy, dreamy spell

O'er a forest vaguely pleasant
　　With the Oomatonga's smell,
And for leagues around him amorous ' Ahkhs ! '
　　Cacophonously swell :
With luck he 'll bag a Vhatka ;
　　　　Who can tell ?

AH, MOMOTOMBO !

Ah, Momotombo, would I might
 Thy distant mountains scan !
Were green Managua's groves in sight—
 How pleasing then life's plan !

Atlas in hand, I watch and wake,
Pining to hear the billows break
 On Desolado's shore.
Sweet were to me their wild refrain—
A deep, a sad, a solemn strain—
 They 'd roar it o'er and o'er.

Alas ! 'tis not my fate to roam,
Not *there* for me is hearth, heath, home ;
 I stay but where I am.
Yet never sighs the halcyon breeze
But whispers of thy tim-tam trees,
 The yookoos in thy yams,
Thy merry little chickadees,
 And clutemnacious clams.

In sleep I creep where, fathoms deep,
 El Paraiso flows ;
Exultant climb at morning-prime
 Tegucigalpa's snows.

With dream-tranced eyes I watch the flies
     Cloud inland, rank on rank.
Borne on the breeze that thrills the seas
That sweep with ease the Caribees,
They swarm with parched proboscides,
Protruding eyes and folded knees,
     Athwart Mosquito Bank.

Alas ! sweet Momotombo—and
     Solentiname's Isle !

But though my grief is past relief,
     And innocent of guile,
Whene'er, with open Gazetteer,
My own enchanting voice I hear
Lisping in accents shrill and clear—
' Agguapadalpo, Yali, Za—
Catacoluca, Paundma,
Chalatenango . . .'—well, la, la !
     I *can't* refrain a smile.

FOXES

Old Dr. Cox's
Love of foxes
Led his steps astray ;
He 'd haunt the woods and coppices,
And lure the beasts away,
Into a bright green private park,
In safety there to *stay*.

Now Dr. Cox's
Dodge with foxes
Was simple as could be ;
For first of all he 'd find an earth,
And mark it with a T
(Just T for Trapper) ; then he 'd wait
Till dusk ; just wait and see.

For Dr. Cox's
Way with foxes
Needed but a *hush* ;
When seated on a bank of loam,
Beneath a tree or bush,
He 'd tootle-ootle on a comb,
And each would bring its brush.

QUICKELS

THE Quickel-fish a-quiver in Parana-tinga river never
    shiver when they hear the shrill ' A-veisse ! '
Of the brave to his old squaw, as he pads on muffled paw,
    up the slopes bestrown with porphyry and gneiss ;
For they see the rose a-blowing, hear the paddles to-and-
    froing, and they know that 's quite impossible in ice.

But when mute upon the mountains fall the well-springs
    and the fountains, where the chamois o'er the
    glacier nimbly sports ;
When through snow-embowered crevasses gallop squad-
    rons of wild asses, seeking herbage 'mid the jasper
    and the quartz ;

Ah then, ah then, alas ! their haunts congeal like glass—
gelidified to crystal are their courts.

O brief, sweet day thus ended ! In a marvellous trance
suspended, they shine like gouts of gold in shimmer-
ing ore—
Like frozen clots of light, amber, opal, malachite—while
their turquoise eyes in terror scan the shore ;
For like cats come Indians stalking ; sounds a baleful
tomahawking ; they chop them out in blocks, and
thirst for more !

THE LION-HUNTER

The lion-hunter is a man
　　Who lives to hunt the lion ;
He 'd gladly hunt him might and main,
Through France and Portugal and Spain,
　　And back to old Albion.

But where there 's Negroes is the place
　　The sun shines hot and dry on—
'Tis there, with spy-glass to his eye,
He takes his camp-stool, no-one by,
And spies about—and spies about—just spies about for
　　lion.

Yes, there he sits, with hat on head—
　　The only hat he 'd try on—
His hat (I mean) of pith with peaks,
And flaps, both sides, to shield the cheeks,
　　Wherein he hunts the lion.

From one oasis to the next,
　　He packs his bag to hie on,
And sometimes his pyjamas share
That bag with hanks of tawny hair—
And these were once—yes, these were once—yes, these
　　were once a lion.

Perchance, at last, this happy man
    Will hunt his way to Zion—
With a golden harp and most beautiful wings
    To play on and to fly on.
But now and again when the music 's done,
He 'll hie to some nook of sand and sun,
And there you 'll find him (with his gun)
    Colloguing with a lion.

QUACK-HUNTING

When evening's darkening azure
　　Stains the water crystal clear,
It 's a marvellous sweet pleasure
　　A small coracle to steer
To where, in reeds and rushes,
　　Squeak and chuckle, sup and suck
A multitudinous company
　　　　Of Duck.

There silver-shining Hesper
　　Smiles at Mars—a solemn red ;
The myriads of the Milky Way
　　Are circling overhead ;
But even though the dusk 's too dim
　　To sheen their wings—with luck
I catch those button eyes and know
　　　　They 're Duck.

Not mine the dismal fowling-piece,
　　The *living* duck for me !
I strow upon the water crumbs
　　Which they, that instant, see ;
They paddle in like steamboats, with
　　Their tails behind their backs ;
And I ?　　I simply sit and count
　　　　Their quacks.

One sigh in that great silence—
  Wild-winged creatures, they 'd be gone ;
But me—I scarcely breathe, I don't,
  But softly sidle on ;
And while the dears are feeding, with
  Their tails behind their backs,
I make my nightly score, I count
   Their quacks.

MARCH HARES

'THE best way to go,' said my muffled-up friend, 'is to
    look in its *form* for a Hare, you know';
So, with gun over shoulder, we sallied out early, the
    bushes all hunched up with snow, you know;
The dawn was still under the eastern horizon, and O
    but the morning was rare, you know;
The elms and the oaks were a-dangle with ice, that
    swayed in the breeze to and fro, you know—
Icicles half a yard long at the least, that tinkled and rang
    in the air, you know;
'A marvellous music,' said I to my friend; and he, he
    never said, No, you know.

The snow had been falling for days, there were drifts full
    fifteen feet deep, and so fair, you know,
Aurora herself might have looked to her blushes, and Cupid
    have trimmed up his bow, you know;
And when o'er the rim of the World came the Sun, and
    with eye like a topaz did glare, you know,
We stood for a while as if blinded with Paradise, dumb in
    that wonderful glow, you know;
We coughed, and we shifted our guns, and went on—no
    more than a cough could we dare, you know,
For moment by moment we couldn't tell where we should
    come within sight of the foe, you know.

And, all of a sudden, my friend, he said, ' 'Ssh ! ' and I
    looked and I listened ; and there, you know—
Not half a shot off, with his ears and his scut, acrouch in
    the lily-white snow, you know,

And his eyes like two blazing bright marbles of glass—sat
    staring and glaring a Hare, you know !
The sun it shone brighter, the blue it grew bluer, the
    heavens like an infinite O, you know,
And a breeze out of nowhere rang sweet as a bell rings,
    and stirred in our whiskers and hair, you know.

My friend—then—he—up—with—his—gun—to—his
　　shoulder—and tugged at the trigger : but lo ! you
　　know,
In his kindness of heart he 'd forgotten to load, for for
　　slaughter he didn't much care, you know ;
We laughed, oh ! laughed we ; and my ghost ! if old Watt
　　didn't up with his nose and cry, ' Ho ! ' you know ;
And stamped for his brothers and sisters to come, and they
　　hopped up in scores from their lair, you know.
They danced, they fandangoed, they scuttered, they sang,
　　turned somersaults, leapfrogged, and so, you know,
We trudged back to breakfast with nothing to jug, which
　　wasn't *exacaly* fair, you know,
　　　　　Which *wasn't* exacaly fair.

WEA

IF I were the Beadle of Weston Weaton,
 A happy old Beadle I 'd be,
Sitting up there in my two-pair-back,
 Looking out on the deep blue sea ;
While a bellying cloud on the West Wind comes
And splashes my scarlet geraniums ;
  And the honey-bee hums,
  As I twiddle my thumbs
And smile at the gables of Wea.

If I were the Beadle of Weston Weaton,
 I 'd have a stuffed dog in a case,
A woolly-haired, brown, retriever dog,
 With amber eyes in his face.
Under the picture of widgeons he 'd stand,
Looking into the parlour, mute and bland,
  On fine yaller sand,
  Stuffed by Indy Shand,
10, High Street, Weston Wea.

As soon as my Birthday (June 9) came round,
 I 'd give all the children a treat ;
Infants like angels at tables on trestles,
 And flags blazing out in the street ;

[105]

Cherries and gingerpop, buns and plum-cake,
Lord ! what huzzaing and clapping they 'd make ;
    And their little hearts break,
    As my way I 'd take,
  Smiling and bowing through Wea !

On Sundays I 'd sprightly step off to the Kirk—
    Neat pepper-and-salt, in tweed,
With a springside boot, silk cravat at my throat,
    Stiff collar—intoning the Creed.
With the ladies and little tots all in a row,
I 'd troll out the hymmums and Psalms, and throw
    A languishing glow
    On a widow I know—
Mrs. James, of the *Chequers*, in Wea.

And I 'd thank my stars, as I climbed the stairs,
    I was born in the parish of Wea,
Where the Burghers are solid respectable folk,
    And the Lord of the Manor a Ffeogh ;
And me be angry with Edward Lear
For his Cheadle limerick ?—Lor, no fear !
    I 'd toast him, I know it,
    For a man and a poet,
If I were the Beadle of Wea.

WITCHCRAFT

A parson I knew in the village of Eard—
Himself like a solemn bespectacled bird—
   Had a witchcraft I 've never seen beat,
For attracting around him small creatures with wings ;
Whatsoever on earth hops, nests, flutters and sings,
   Would flit at his call to his feet.

A whistled decoy-note, and out there would hie,
From the tops of his trees, stables, chimneypots, sky,
A host of small birds, and, all twittering come,
Not in hope of cheese, fat, worms, seed, water or crumb,

But merely for joy of himself, and to share
In the open of heaven his company there.

I 've sat with my friend in the twilight and seen
The whimbrels at play in the glim,
And owls large and small hooting out of the green,
And it seemed they were calling to him.
And he 'd sidle his head o'er his book, and you knew
That its print now said naught but Too-whit and to-hoo :
    And it couldn't say sweeter to him.

And often, with candle in hand, he has said,
As we climbed up the staircase to go off to bed,
' I like, Jones, to think they 'll sing on when I 'm dead.
    And wherever I happen to be,
Should it chance but an echo of music should come
Such as now I delight in, I 'll post away home—
    I couldn't resist it, you see.

' Besides, Jones, a secret,' he muttered it low,
In the gleam his round spectacles all of a glow,
' Soft down 's on my shoulder-blades sprouting, I vow ;
And even the primaries stirring, and so,
    The flight will come easy to me ! '
With a chuckle he clutched at my elbow, and I—
    I confess I was bound to agree.

So we laid him to rest where, in green month of May,
A group of young hawthorns would perfume the day,
 And there, if you happen to pass,
You will hear morn and evening, and middle-day too,
The wild birds lamenting the friend they all knew ;
 And even when midnight 's o'erhead,
In the midst of the may-blossom—silent as snow—
When all throats are hushed, sobs a voice sweet with woe,
 The nightingale's voice, it is said.

FINIS

THIS Mouse is here
(As the cut makes clear),
For to prove, whatsoever else fails,
That Providence sends
The mite *two* ends—
The tip of his snout and his tail's.